SHIRE NATURAL

C000311615

THE SWALLOW

PETER TATE

CONTENTS

COVER: *A female Swallow bringing food to her nest in an old farm building. Her very white underparts and slightly shorter tail streamers distinguish her from the male. Her throat is full of insect food for her brood.*

Series editors: Jim Flegg and Chris Humphries

Set in 9 point Times roman and printed in Great Britain by C. I. Thomas & Sons (Haverfordwest) Ltd, Press Buildings, Merlins Bridge, Haverfordwest, Dyfed.

The Swallow family

The European Swallow *(Hirundo rustica),* known in North America as the Barn Swallow, is a member of the Hirundinidae, a family consisting of some seventy-five species divided among seventeen genera. Although the popular names of the family refer to swallows and martins the distinction has no taxonomic significance. They have a virtually worldwide distribution, occurring in all the continents with the exception of Antarctica, but they are not found in the northern polar regions or the most arid of deserts.

Apart from a small number of species such as the Cliff Swallow *(Hirundo pyrrhonota)* of North America and the Banded Martin *(Riparia cincta)* of Africa, all swallows have forked tails of varying depth. This characteristic elongated outer tail forming 'streamers' is most pronouncedly developed in the Blue Swallow of Africa *(Hirundo atrocaerulea),* a species which is atypical of the family in that it is almost uniformly coloured, a feature it shares with the Purple Martin *(Progne subis)* and Black Saw-wing Swallow *(Psalidoprocne holomelas).* The majority are brightly coloured, with metallic blue and red colours predominating, frequently combined with prominent pale rumps, while some, such as the Sand and Crag Martins, have a rather drab, brownish plumage. All have small feet and legs and those species which nest in holes in the earth also possess strong claws.

In general the family forms a closely knit group within which hybrids can quite easily occur, such as those between the House Martin and the European Swallow, the Barn Swallow and the Cave Swallow *(Petrochelidon pyrronota)* in North America, and possibly the European Swallow and the Red-rumped Swallow *(Hirundo daurica).* It is impossible to determine accurately how frequently such hybridisation takes place, but the fact that it has been observed suggests that it is not as rare an event as it is with less genetically homogenous bird families.

As far as is known, no swallow species has become extinct, and of the seventy-five species known, only three can be considered to be endangered. The rare Jamaican Golden Swallow *(Kalochelidon euchrysea)* is one of two subspecies, the other of which occurs only in Hispaniola, where it is very local. The Red Sea Cliff Swallow *(Hirundo perdita)* is known only from one specimen discovered in 1984, so it must either be extremely rare or very local not to have been discovered earlier by one of the many ornithological expeditions to north-east Africa, where it is presumed to breed. It is very similar to the African Cliff Swallow *(Hirundo spilodera)* and is probably closely related to that species. Another mysterious swallow is the White-eyed River Martin *(Pseudochelidon sirintarae),* which was first found in Thailand in 1968 and of which, despite further searches, few others have been seen and none since 1980. Its breeding locality is still unknown. Together with its only known relative, the African River Martin *(Pseudochelidon eurystomina),* these River Martins form an aberrant genus within the Hirundinidae.

HABITAT AND FOOD

The swallow's preferred habitat is open countryside, farmland, river banks and valleys, lakes and savannah country; areas of dense forest, desert and seashores are generally avoided. A number of species such as the Sand Martin, Purple Martin and North American Cliff Swallow nest in colonies. The European Swallow may choose a solitary nesting site or, alternatively will form a loose-knit colony around a farm. Such a colony usually consists of fewer than ten nests, but over twenty have been recorded. Old-fashioned farmyards with stables and cowbyres, barns and broken-down sheds offer the most suitable sites but are becoming increasingly difficult for the swallow to find.

Nesting strategy varies considerably within the family. Some species such as the Sand Martin nest in holes which they excavate themselves in cliffs, whilst others build enclosed mud nests supported on man-made structures, such as shelves and beams, preferably those posi-

1. *A male Swallow holding a large insect in its bill. The long outer tail feathers and the white subterminal marks on the tail are well displayed.*

tioned in such a way that they are protected from above. The Tree Swallow of North America traditionally nests in holes in old trees but quickly adapts to making use of buildings, suitable cavitites or boxes provided either deliberately or fortuitously by man.

With the exception of an American species, the Tree Swallow *(Tachycineta bicolor)*, which sometimes eats bayberries, as a family the swallows are almost entirely insectivorous, their prey usually being taken in flight although sometimes, but rarely, whilst perched. The swallow's short bill with its wide gape and rictal bristles around the beak is ideally adapted for catching flying insects, whilst its large wing area in ratio to its weight renders it extremely manoeuvrable in flight. The European Swallow takes the great majority of its food at low levels, often just skimming the ground usually at a distance of 6 feet (1.8 metres) or less above the surface, whilst the House Martin takes its smaller prey at higher levels.

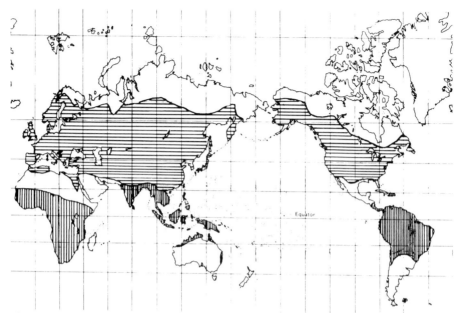

2. *Map showing the breeding range (horizontal lines) and the main wintering areas (vertical lines) of the Swallow.*

Swallows drink by flying very low over the surface of the water, dipping in their bills and scooping up the liquid. Bathing is carried out by lightly immersing their bodies in the water, although on a very few occasions they have been observed to dust-bath like the Sparrows. At Victoria Falls in Africa Swallows have been seen bathing in the spray from the falls.

MIGRATION AND MORTALITY

Many of the swallow species are migratory to a greater or lesser degree and the European Swallow, the species with which this book is mainly concerned, is a long-distance migrant over almost the whole of its range. Generally those that breed furthest north travel furthest south for the non-breeding season, but the subspieces *(Hirundo rustica savignii)* which occurs in Egypt is, unlike the rest of the species, sedentary. Some tropical swallows are resident, whilst others carry out comparatively short migratory journeys in response to some particularly

unfavourable circumstance such as the rainy season.

Taken as a family the swallows are successful, but some species are liable to considerable population fluctuations. These can occur as a result of climatic disasters such as occurred in 1931 and 1974, when birds migrating from northern Europe were trapped by unseasonable snowfalls and prolonged torrential rain whilst crossing the Alps. On both these occasions many thousands of birds were rescued and flown, or taken by train, from Switzerland to either Italy or Nice. Similarly many birds suffer a particularly heavy mortality rate whilst crossing the most arid parts of the Sahara desert. Other natural disasters such as tropical storms and tornadoes like those at Upemba in Zaire have also killed immense numbers on occasions. In January 1961 the Bredasdorp area of Cape Province suffered a sudden intensely cold spell and large numbers of swallows were found clustered together in barns. Many became torpid and later died. Such tor-

4

pidity results when, because of a shortage of food, it becomes impossible to maintain the body heat and the body temperature drops between 10 and 20 degrees Fahrenheit. This form of hypothermia is occasionally reversed but generally results in death. The European Swallow appears to be rather delicate in this respect and during a cold spell in Zimbabwe many of this species were found to be torpid and dying whilst other species seemed to be hardly affected.

Less spectacular but more insidious causes of falls in population numbers are probably brought about by changes in agricultural practices and the increased use of pesticides, the presence of which produces more damage by reducing the the food supply of insects available to the birds than by actual direct poisoning. The disastrous effects of spraying against insects in farm buildings was proved by a survey undertaken in Germany which showed a swallow nestling mortality of 76 per cent as against 22 per cent in unsprayed buildings.

The common birds census organised by the British Trust for Ornithology shows

3. *A male Barn Swallow (Hirundo rustica erythrogaster) showing the russet underparts.*

considerable fluctuations in Swallow numbers from year to year, and whilst it is difficult to obtain a precise picture for Britain and Europe as a whole, a small overall decrease may be perceived since the 1950s. This, however, does not approach the catastrophic decline in the European populations of the Sand Martin *(Riparia riparia)*, whose breeding population, following a steady decrease over several years, fell by 70 per cent between 1983 and 1984.

Plumage and field marks

The European Swallow *(Hirundo rustica rustica)* has uniform blue-black upper parts, often showing a metallic sheen; the forehead, chin and throat are chestnut red and the throat is separated from the rest of the underparts by a dark blue pectoral band. The underparts are white, although in the North American race *(Hirundo rustica erythrogaster)* they are rusty red. The tail is deeply forked and its outer feathers, especially in the adult male, are greatly elongated, forming 'streamers'. The tail feathers have white sub-terminal markings which show up clearly when the tail is spread out. Albinos have been occasionally recorded.

In order to provide good binocular vision, necessary for accurately judging distances when catching small insects, the eyes are set slightly more forward than with many small birds but not so pronouncedly as in the owls or birds of prey. The inner construction of the eye, with two especially sensitive areas of the retina called temporal fovea, is a feature which it shares with the hawks and hummingbirds and greatly increases its visual acuity. The bill is broad and flat, with a wide gape to facilitate catching aerial prey. The legs are short and well adapted for perching and clinging to the nest but not suitable for easy walking.

Male Swallows are slightly larger than females, with wings 120 to 129 mm (4.7 to 5 inches) long as compared with 116 to 128 mm (4.5 to 5 inches) for the females. The outer tail feathers measure from 93 to 122 mm (3.6 to 4.8 inches) in males, but are much shorter in females and juveniles, where they vary between 76 and 107 mm (3 and 4.2 inches) and 60 and 64 mm (2.4 and 2.5 inches) respectively. Females tend to have whiter underparts than males and the throat band is a less vivid shade of blue. Juveniles are duller in colour and lack the characteristic metallic blue sheen; the chestnut parts are more brownish in hue and the base of the bill is pale yellow.

FLIGHT

The Swallow's flight is low and dashing, sweeping over the ground often only inches above the surface. They may occasionally fly and feed around rooftop level but rarely go much higher. The wing beats are shallow, interspersed with glides and rapid changes of direction when in pursuit of aerial prey. They are amongst the smallest birds to combine energy-saving gliding with their normal flapping flight to any appreciable extent. For example, in sustained flight a House Martin expends less than half the energy used by a comparable passerine bird. Because it is a small bird and flies low the Swallow gives the impression of greater speed than it actually achieves. A serious experiment in the United States, using sophisticated radar equipment, gave an average cross-wind speed of 17 mph (27 km/h), with a speed of 16.7 mph (26.9 km/h) against a headwind, and 22.2 mph (35.7 km/h) downwind. The maximum speed recorded was 35 mph (56 km/h). All figures were lower than might have been expected.

SONG

The Swallow's song is very simple and, although rather unmusical, it has a cheerful quality. Swallows mostly sing on the wing but also sometimes when perched, especially on telephone wires or a television aerial near to the nest. Exceptionally a Swallow may sing from the ground. They sing more often early in the day, sometimes in a communal song flight at dawn, when a number of birds may climb up high into the sky, singing during their flight. Their song may be heard through-

4. *A pair of Swallows at their nest. The shorter tail streamers of the female on the left show clearly.*

5. *A barn with a dark interior, a favourite nesting habitat.*

out the breeding season.

Their vocabulary of calls is small. The warning call, used by the birds when mobbing a potential enemy such as a cat or a roosting owl, is best described as a high-pitched staccato 'tswee'. On returning to the nest the adult announces its arrival with a sharp disyllabic 'tschwick' call, whilst in flight Swallows frequently give a monosyllabic 'tswik', which would appear to be a possible contact call.

FOOD

Early in the season eight out of ten insects taken by Swallows are flies, preferably large-bodied ones such as blue and green bottles, stable flies, hover and horse flies. For some unknown reason they are reluctant to take dung flies. In bad weather when a sufficient number of these is not available, smaller prey such as greenfly and lacewing moths is eaten and occasionally, when the air temperature is too low for more suitable flying insects, bees: only the stingless drone bees are taken as the Swallow lacks the ability to remove stings from workers or queens. Similarly, under difficult conditions Swallows have been known to take torpid flies from thistles, certain moth caterpillars which hang suspended below twigs by threads, flies from rotting seaweed on a beach and even decaying vegetable matter or bread put out for other birds.

It has been estimated that a half-grown brood of Swallows needs on average some six thousand insects a day. This means that some 150,000 items of prey are needed in order to raise one nestling. An average brood will thus require half a million insects, to which must be added those insects taken by the adult birds for their own needs.

Because the type of insects available varies during the course of the summer the composition of the food provided for the nestlings undergoes considerable changes. Second broods are generally mainly fed on greenfly and barklice, fewer caterpillars are taken, and by the end of the breeding season large flies form only a tenth or so of the prey. This enforced change of diet means that the adult birds have to work very much harder in order to provide the quantity of food required by the nestlings. Around one hundred small insects have to be

8

captured as against fifteen to twenty larger ones to supply the equivalent amount of food for each meal.

HABITAT

The adult birds usually prefer, whenever possible, to remain within a few hundred yards of the nest when hunting for food. This is easier if they have been able to find a 'traditional' site such as an old-fashioned farmyard whose stockyards, stables and manure heaps all provide plentiful quantities of insect food. A Danish study has shown a direct correlation between a decline in milk and beef production and the number of Swallows, and a similar study of British agriculture would probably produce much the same results. With no large open middens in modern pig units or dairy farms and consequently many fewer flies, it follows that the Swallow is forced to spend a much greater part of its time flying considerable distances over the meadows and surrounding countryside in search of insects. The modern system of arable farming, with large fields planted with cereal crops and heavily sprayed against all insect pests, provides comparatively poor opportunities for Swallows to feed. The House Martins and Swifts, which feed on smaller insect prey at a greater height, seem to be less affected by such changes.

NESTING SITES

For the Swallow to breed successfully the construction and condition of the chosen farm building is a significant, if not crucial, factor. Dilapidated stables, cowbyres and barns provide numerous dark ledges, nooks and crannies which are ideally suited to the bird's needs. Entry through a broken window or badly fitting barn door presents no difficulties to a bird capable of such highly agile flight. Observations have shown that an aperture 2 by 2¾ inches (50 by 57 mm) is large enough for a Swallow to fly through regularly. Farm buildings consisting of metal framework covered by corrugated sheeting of the type often erected since the Second World War do not provide nearly so many suitable ledges and brackets and this sort of large unit does not appeal to a bird which prefers to nest close to an entrance. Moreover such buildings permit plenty of daylight to enter, a further deterrent to a bird which favours a rather dark nest site. A Danish study has revealed that of the Swallows' nests observed 83 per cent received less than 300 lux and of these 55 per cent received less than 100 lux. Predation is far more likely to occur in a more brightly lit nest site, with rats, Jackdaws and particularly domestic cats being the main enemies.

Evidence from the United States indicates that the nestlings are far more likely to succumb to heat beneath a modern, less well insulated roof which cannot offer the protection provided by the old tiled and wood structures — a serious matter when one considers the Swallows' predilection for building their nests close to the roof of any building.

Sometimes, like many other species, Swallows will utilise an exceptional nest site and among the more bizarre locations recorded have been an old Robin's nest, a hat hanging on a stable wall and the pelmet of a curtain in a bedroom. Exceptionally, they will build a cup-like nest against a wall or rock surface in the style of a House Martin, possibly the kind of nest they might have built before man-made buildings became available. Very rarely Swallows' nests have been found in trees. An example of this was reported in Flanders during the First World War, when twelve nests were built in a shattered poplar tree, every building around it having been reduced to a heap of rubble. Under much the same circumstances a number of nests were also found in underground dugouts. Swallows have also been found nesting below ground level in disused mines in Cornwall and in caves in Ireland. In Britain a nest has been discovered built in a thatched roof, without any mud being used, and another, of similar construction, in a crevice in some stone slabs some 18 inches (460 mm) above the ground.

The usual site of a Swallow's nest, within a building and close to a roof, makes it an unlikely host for the Cuckoo. Nevertheless instances of Cuckoos being raised by Swallows have been reported in

Somerset in 1951 and Staffordshire in 1972. These are very unusual occurrences, and in the case of the nest in Staffordshire there was circumstantial evidence to show that the Swallow's nest had been mistaken by the Cuckoo for that of a Pied Wagtail nearby.

Breeding

COURTSHIP AND DISPLAY

The Swallows' annual cycle begins with their arrival in the north. The majority of the earliest arrivals are the older experienced males, which, if they have bred previously, will usually return to a former nesting site, possibly even to the same nest. Young males which have not bred before are likely to return to the same general area as that in which they were raised, but their later arrival means they have fewer opportunities of finding the most suitable nest sites and consequently reduces their chances of breeding successfully. The females generally arrive a few days after the males and are less likely to return to a specific area.

The male chooses the nest site and having done so advertises his choice by circling around its immediate vicinity at a height of some 150 feet (50 metres), singing his twittering song and inviting the attention of any female who may be present and is seeking a mate. On seeing another Swallow approach, the male sweeps down to the chosen location and, if the new arrival is a female, perches on the nest site while making a series of pecking movements. If the female shows interest and stays he will then commence his courtship display.

Although the Swallow is a relatively common bird and reasonably tolerant of man, the display leading to copulation has rarely been described and there may well be gaps in our knowledge concerning the precise details of this. A form of display which has been observed involves the male bird indulging in a very slow, wavering, circling flight below the nest site, with tail spread and feet left dangling. However, this 'circling display' is not necessarily a prelude to courtship and may take place at almost any stage in the breeding cycle. An alternative form of display has been reported in which a Swallow glided slowly above his potential mate which was perched on a telegraph wire. Another male was seen to perch alongside the female, stretching his body forward with the chestnut feathers of his chin and forehead fluffed out but the rest of his plumage drawn in and sleek, while the female solicited him by leaning forwards horizontally, holding her folded wings away from her body.

NEST BUILDING

The construction of the nest is undertaken by both birds, frequently working together as a team and helping each other to lay in place the mud pellets of which the nest is composed. It is the female, however, which completes the final stages by lining the nest with feathers.

The nest is built of mud collected by the birds from nearby puddles. This is formed into small lozenges in the bird's mouth and throat and laid in the same pattern as bricks to form the walls of the nest. Often little pieces of straw are taken with the mud, or pieces of animal hair or rootlets are brought separately and pushed into the mud as reinforcement. The quantity of mud brought on each visit is surprisingly large and a bird has been seen to take more than a dozen bites into the mud before returning to the nest with its throat bulging.

The time taken to construct the nest varies between six and twelve days. In very wet weather when the mud takes longer to dry out building is slower, since if the birds build too much at one time before the mud dries out a disastrous collapse may occur. Either for this reason or in order to recuperate their energy, the birds take frequent rests between bouts of mud gathering and building. Building activity is greatest in the early hours of the day when as many as twenty-eight visits per hour may be made to the nest, while as few as five visits per hour may be made between six and nine o'clock in the evening.

For the second brood a pair will

6. *An unusual nest site.*

7. *A Swallow collecting mud for its nest.*

8. *The nest and eggs of a pair of Swallows.*

9. *Five juvenile Swallows at about fifteen days old.*

10. *An immature Swallow with duller plumage and a shorter tail than the adult.*

generally use a different nest; often re-utilising an old one from a previous year, but sometimes an entirely new one will be constructed. This is to avoid too great a build-up of parasites such as lice in the nest, which can easily happen during too long an occupancy. It is the nestlings which are most at risk from these blood-sucking parasites. A study made in Holland showed that as many as 20 per cent of the birds were infected, the majority of which were nestlings, but in most cases no great harm seemed to have been done.

LAYING AND INCUBATION

Egg laying commences within a day or two of the completion of the nest. In southern Britain eggs are laid from around the end of April (unless the weather is unusually cold), reaching a peak from mid May to mid June, with a second peak for the second brood in the first three weeks of July. In the north of England and Scotland the dates are usually about a week later.

The female lays her eggs on successive days, usually in the early morning. The eggs have a white background finely spotted with red brown and ashy markings. The average size is 20 by 13.75 mm (about ¾ by ½ inch). There is conflicting evidence as to whether incubation commences with the laying of the first egg or when the clutch is complete. The young take between fourteen and sixteen days to hatch, the average time being 15.3 days.

The normal clutch is four or five; six is not unusual and eight have been recorded, but in this latter and exceptional case the possibility of a second female using the same nest should not be discounted.

Although the Swallow normally rears two broods, if the circumstances are sufficiently favourable a third is sometimes also raised. This is more likely to occur in the southern part of the birds' range. A third brood is usually smaller than the previous ones with an average of around 3.5 eggs.

Taking the Swallow population in the western Palearctic region as a whole, the size of clutch increases and the number of broods decrease with the latitude: the further north they breed the larger the number of eggs laid per clutch but the smaller the number of broods. The reasons for this are comlex but evidence exists to show that clutch size is regulated by such factors as the length of the daylight during which the young can be fed, the availability of food and the energy requirements of the nestlings. The lower the temperature the more food the young require to maintain both temperature and growth.

DEVELOPMENT OF THE NESTLINGS

At the time of hatching the nestlings are practically devoid of down and require constant brooding by the adults. Both parents participate in this task with the female undertaking the greater share, some 65 per cent of the daylight hours and the whole of the night. As the young grow, the amount of brooding required decreases steadily until by the ninth day it is needed only during the night and about 7 per cent of daylight hours, and thereafter at night only.

Time spent in the nest between hatching and flight varies between seventeen and twenty-four days, depending upon weather conditions and the availability of food. As the nestlings grow the work required from the adults to provide for their brood increases considerably. Observations taken at one nest showed that during the first day eleven visits an hour were made, rising to around fifty visits an hour by the fourteenth day, after which the rate of feeding visits declined.

Both the adult birds share the task of feeding the nestlings. In some instances the young of the first brood have also been seen helping to feed their younger siblings and additionally, although such behaviour is probably exceptional, helping their parents to build the second nest.

The nestlings gain weight rapidly. From an initial weight of about 2.5 grams (0.089 ounce) at hatching, they reach around 23 grams (0.89 ounce) by the twelfth day, with a growth rate for the first ten days of as much as 2.5 grams (0.089 ounce) a day. After about the fourteenth day the net weight of the nestlings falls to around 16 to 18 grams (0.57 to 0.63 ounce). The fall in weight at

11. *A typical nest site on a beam close to the roof.*

this stage is due to a greater expenditure of energy as the young birds begin to stretch and exercise their wings, preen their feathers and become generally more active.

The nestlings' body temperature increases from about 92.5 Fahrenheit (33.6 Celsius) at one day old to 106 Fahrenheit (41 Celsius) at the fourteenth day, rising by the twentieth day to the normal figure of 108 Fahrenheit (42.2 Celsius). Complete temperature control is not achieved until the maximum body weight has been reached. These figures give only an indication of the usual course of events, there being as always a great deal of variation between different broods depending on weather conditions and the food available.

At sometime around the fifth day after hatching the flight feathers begin to appear through the skin, by the ninth day the tail feather tips begin to sprout and by the thirteenth day most of the body feathers are appearing. Some nestlings are ready for flight by the eighteenth day and most have left the nest by the twentieth to twenty-second day.

MOULT

Following the breeding season it is customary for the majority of bird species to begin a progressive moult to replace those feathers whose efficiency has been diminished by wear and abrasion, a condition much aggravated by the task of hatching and raising their young.

Because they have to fly some 6000 miles (9600 km) to their winter quarters Swallows cannot allow their capacity for flight to be impaired. Although a small number of individuals do begin to moult their primary flight feathers before departure, and a few have been observed to have started their moult before reaching their final destination, for most Swallows moult is suspended until after they have completed their migration to Africa. The duration of moult in Africa is variable and leisurely, especially among the juveniles, whose moult may well not have been entirely completed when the time comes for them to return north to their breeding areas.

Migration

That swallows do migrate is today such a universally acknowledged fact that anyone who otherwise knows very little about birds would probably be able to name the swallow as a migratory bird. Such certainty has not always existed. From the time of Aristotle in the third century BC until the end of the eighteenth century there was controversy and speculation as to whether the birds did migrate or simply hibernated in the mud beneath ponds and lakes. This particular myth probably arose from the swallows' habit of roosting in reedbeds in the autumn prior to their departure. When the birds disappeared it was not difficult

12. Swallows and House Martins collecting on telephone wires prior to migration.

13. *The Striped Swallow (Hirundo abyssinica) of southern Africa.*

to assume that they had simply crept down to the bottom of the lake, there to await the spring. Such surmise was further reinforced by the behaviour pattern of the birds themselves, which when they return in the spring can frequently be seen hawking for insects over lakes and streams, where they tend to be particularly numerous at that time of the year.

The majority of Swallows leave southern Britain in late September and early October, although a very few may linger on until early December. Very exceptionally a single bird will attempt to overwinter and may even succeed, as occurred at Marazion in Cornwall during the winter of 1974/5.

Before their migration in the autumn there is a strong tendency amongst the juveniles to indulge in what appears to be 'random dispersal', with numbers of birds

flying off in a northerly direction, directly opposite to that which their migration route would normally follow — a behaviour pattern which can be confusing to the casual observer. In Gibraltar in September it is possible to watch a steady stream of Swallows flying northwards, whilst at the same time small flocks are going south. Similar northward flights have been reported from the eastern shores of the Baltic. Because on the autumn migration the Swallows generally move in smallish groups, possibly as family parties, the suggestion has been made that these 'dispersal flights' are a form of training for the young birds, but as yet there is no evidence to support this theory.

Another variation of migration flights is that which is referred to as 'redirected passage', an example of this being that of

17

a female Swallow which arrived in Lincolnshire in May and was then recaptured in Potsdam in East Germany a month later.

Since the start of an organised ringing scheme, first set up in Britain in 1909, returns have yielded a great deal of important information as to the routes and winter quarters of the European Swallow. By a remarkable coincidence only three years after this scheme was inaugurated, and at a time when few birds had been individually marked, a Swallow ringed in Cheadle, Staffordshire, in May 1911 was recovered from a farm near Utrecht, Natal, in December 1912. Some seventy years later, by December 1984, no less than 884,820 Swallows had been ringed in Britain, of which 6520 had been recovered. Although this figure only represents a low percentage of recoveries, and inevitably there are still gaps in the overall migratory pattern, with a great many questions still unanswered as to the exact locality and areas where the different populations spend their winter, nevertheless these numbers are sufficient to establish a reasonably accurate picture.

There is now firm evidence that individual Swallows have a definite tendency to return to the same area in the southern hemisphere in successive years, much as they do to their breeding sites in the north. There is also evidence to show that, possibly because of climatic changes, there has been a gradual shift in areas used by specific populations. For example, the primary wintering areas for Swallows which breed in Britain lie in the south-eastern part of the Republic of South Africa, but since the 1960s there is some indication that there has been a tendency for their winter range to extend further to the south and west into Cape Province.

Taking the migratory habits of the species as a whole, it seems that birds which breed in different parts of the northern hemisphere also winter in sepa-

14. *Swallows and martins hawking insects whilst on migration in Jordan.*

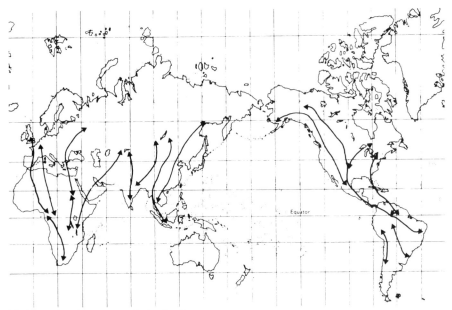

15. *The migration routes of the Swallow.*

rate and distinct areas: Swallows which have bred in Germany spend their winters in Zaire; many birds from the Soviet Union fly further to the south, but those from the Black Sea regions stay further to the north, in Uganda, whilst Swallows from southern Spain barely cross the equator and small numbers of birds regularly winter in parts of Africa north of the equator. To add to this confused and seemingly illogical pattern, birds from Holland and Belgium have been recovered in winter from widely scattered areas over southern Africa.

Once established at their winter quarters, the Swallows gather in great flocks at sunset before going to roost. One such group using a reedbed roost in the Transvaal has been estimated at around a million birds, although most of the known roosts are considerably smaller than this. At sunrise the birds leave in great flocks before dividing into smaller numbers in order to feed. In an attempt to extend our knowledge of the Swallows' movements during their non-breeding season and to discover more about the birds' locations and activities in general, an extensive trapping and ringing programme is being carried out at such roosts by ornithologists in southern Africa.

ROUTES

From ringing recoveries of birds trapped or found dead in transit it is becoming increasingly clear which particular routes are taken by the Swallows on their journey to southern Africa. The great majority of birds from Britain follow a direct route through western France, across the Pyrenees and down the east coast of Spain across Morocco and Nigeria to Cameroon. From there they take a more south-easterly direction across the Congo into Botswana and the Republic of South Africa. Others take a more westerly route through West Africa, and British ringed birds have been recovered in Ghana, the Ivory Coast, Rio de Oro and Liberia. Occasionally a single bird has been found wintering in West Africa. A number of Swallows from Britain migrate further to the east, and birds have been recovered from Italy, Malta,

19

16. *A Blue Swallow (Hirundo atrocaerulea) at the entrance to its nest hole.*

Tunisia and Uganda, although the exact proportion of birds which use this route is still unclear.

The normal time taken for a Swallow to complete its journey back from South Africa to Britain is probably around six weeks, but the total period over which migration is spread, that is, the time which elapses between the departure of the earliest and latest birds, is likely to be five months or even longer. The first birds leave South Africa in late January and begin to arrive in Gibraltar around 13th February. Amongst these there may well be some individual birds which overwinter considerably nearer to the equator.

At first movement across Europe is slow, with a small vanguard reaching the south of France around mid March. Thereafter, depending on the weather conditions, progress is swifter and by the beginning of April the birds are crossing central France, Switzerland and southern Germany. The movement of the birds across Europe roughly corresponds to the 48 Fahrenheit isotherm, which means that within a given latitude the birds will arrive earlier on the milder west side of the continent than in the colder eastern regions.

Whilst on migration Swallows appear to fly with a determination and purpose apparently lacking in their unhurried sweeping and swooping flight when simply hunting for food. They would also seem to exhibit considerably more urgency during their northward passage as compared to their somewhat leisurely progress south in the autumn.

In Britain the main body of Swallows usually appears at least two weeks after the first comers and they continue to arrive often well into May. Their appearance in large numbers is likely to be delayed by cold, wet and unseasonable weather. Such conditions bring migration virtually to a halt: the birds are forced to concentrate their efforts on obtaining insect food from around any sheltered lake or marshy area that they can find in the vicinity.

20

Since it is virtually impossible to know when a particular bird commenced its journey and the exact time of arrival at its destination, precise speed of migration is extremely difficult to assess. The best information so far available is that of a Swallow ringed near Pretoria and recovered in Kemerov in the Soviet Union, some 7500 miles (12,069 km) away, thirty-four days later. This would indicate an average rate of progress of about 210 miles (338 km) a day, assuming that the swallow left immediately after it was ringed and was caught as soon as it arrived in Russia. There is further evidence, admittedly circumstantial, of a Swallow which was colour-marked at Rosherville near Pretoria on 3rd April 1966 being seen at Portaferry in Ulster on 23rd April, but as the bird was only sighted and not actually caught proof of its identity cannot be absolutely certain. If true it would have flown about 300 miles (482 km) a day.

Since migratory Swallows do not as a rule fly in a directly straight line between their points of departure and arrival, it follows that, allowing for such deviations from their route, the total mileage accomplished each day must be considerably greater than the above figures might seem to indicate.

THE BARN SWALLOWS OF NORTH AMERICA

The main wintering areas of the Barn Swallows of North America lie within the vast spaces of South America, between Colombia in the west and Guyana in the east, and extend southwards to central Argentina and Chile. Again distance of migration varies widely, some birds going no further than southern central America while a few fly to the southermost part of the continent. Their return journey follows a similar pattern to that of their cousins in the old world, with the first birds arriving in the far south and south-east of the United States in late February and reaching the north of their range by the middle of May, but as in Europe their progress north across the continent is very uneven.

The Swallow, with its several races, has a distribution which encompasses virtually the whole of the northern hemisphere besides occupying a vast wintering area in the southern hemisphere. In addition to southern Africa and South America, other winter ranges are in India and south-east Asia, such areas being occupied by the Swallows which breed in the eastern part of the Soviet Union, China and Japan.

Legend and folklore

Fossil evidence from Ightham in Kent suggests that the Swallow has lived in Britain since at least the Pleistocene age. However, the arrival of man together with his domestic animals and buildings probably provided a more favourable environment for a bird which profits from living in proximity to man.

Because of its familiarity, its beauty and its activities, wholly beneficial to man, an extensive body of folklore has grown up around the Swallow, and its return in spring has for centuries been eagerly anticipated. In Westphalia, for instance, it was considered to be of sufficient importance for the farmer and his family to await its first appearance at the farm gate and then throw open the barn doors to encourage it to enter. In Hesse, watchmen were stationed on church towers to signal the arrival of the first Swallow, whereupon the news was announced by the local magistrates.

Because its return to the northern hemisphere coincides with the beginning of spring, legends abound which link the Swallow's arrival with the various religious festivals which fall at that time of the year. The conviction was widely held that on 25th March, the Feast of the Annunciation, the Swallows fly down from paradise to bring warmth to the earth, and in southern Germany in particular it was firmly believed that the birds would be sure to arrive in time to be present at this festival.

Since it has been seen that the time of arrival varies considerably throughout Europe, the particular saint's day or festival on which the birds are presumed to appear also changes. In Bergamo, for example, they are expected to arrive by St Gregory's Day (12th March), whilst nearby but still in Italy it was thought to be St Joseph's Day (19th March). In Brittany it was believed that the Swallows always return on Maundy Thursday in order to participate in the celebration of Easter.

Legends abound concerning the supposed close connection between the Swallow and the Crucifixion. In Spain and several other European countries it was believed that the red patches on the Swallows' foreheads and throats were the result of their attempts to remove the thorns from Christ's crown as he hung upon the cross; in Portugal they were thought to originate from the Swallows' efforts to wipe away the blood from Christ's wounds. In parts of Russia the story went that the Swallows tried to remove the nails from the cross, and in Sweden that they attempted by their twittering to console Christ during his agony.

In the Austrian Tyrol there is a legend that the Swallows helped God to build the sky and in parts of the Middle East the Swallow, along with other birds, is held to be a bird of paradise to whom the gates of Eden are perpetually open. In the same part of the world it was believed that it was a Swallow which reunited Adam and Eve after their expulsion from the Garden of Eden and that therefore they should always be welcome in any man's home.

There are numerous stories which explain how the Swallow came to acquire its deeply forked tail. One of these recounts that it was a Swallow which first brought fire to the peoples of the earth by stealing it from the devil, but that as it flew away with the fire, the devil threw a firebrand at it and the red marks on its head and forked tail show where it was burned.

A similar tale tells how Satan entrusted a sparrow to guard the fire and as the Swallow swooped down to steal it, the sparrow managed to pluck some feathers from the Swallow's tail as it flew away. From Siberia the Buryut people recount how Tengri, the sky god, fired an arrow at the Swallow when he discovered it stealing fire, hitting the bird's tail and destroying the middle feathers. Yet another fable tells how, in the Garden of Eden, the wicked serpent Eblish snapped at the Swallow's tail and left it forked.

In the Far East similarly the Swallow is highly regarded and the subject of many legends. In Japan it is believed to bring good fortune, and on the day when the birds return in spring it is thought proper for offerings to be made to the household gods to ensure the fertility of the women in the house. In China it was believed that a Swallow brought the egg from heaven which the founder of the Shang dynasty swallowed in order to conceive. The Chinese also thought that the birds brought good luck and in many parts of the country special ledges were built to encourage them to nest.

Legends concerning Swallows are much scarcer in North America, but the Inuit peoples have a belief that Ravens will not molest the nest of a Swallow, and in some parts it was thought that the spirits of dead children come back to earth in the form of Swallows, returning to build their nests by the rocks where they had played as children in a previous existence. The Swallows' twittering song was supposed to resemble the chattering of children.

The affection in which the Swallow is held is almost universal except amongst the Scots and Irish. In both these countries it was thought that the Swallow had some of the devil's blood in its veins. A possible source for this belief is that it may be confused with the Swift (*Apus apus*), which is widely held to be the devil's bird, probably because of its black plumage and its habit of forming into small parties, which race around the roof tops emitting shrill screaming calls as they fly.

The idea of the 'Swallow stone' forms a large part of the myth connected with these birds. The concept of a magical 'Swallow stone' in many ways parallels the belief that there is a magic stone to be found inside the head of a toad, and both

17. Mist netting Swallows at night at a South African roost as part of a ringing programme.

legends probably spring from a common source. One version of this story states that the Swallow knows the whereabouts of a magic pebble which possesses the power to cure blindness. If anyone wishes to obtain such a stone he must first blind the nestlings in the Swallows' nest; then as soon as the mother discovers that her young are blind she will fly to a secret place and bring back the magic stone. In order to trick the bird into giving up the stone a red cloth has to be placed beneath the nest so that when the Swallow has cured her nestlings' blindness, thinking that the red cloth is a fire, she will drop the stone on to the cloth. Once procured the stone was thought to be capable of curing epilepsy as well as blindness.

In an alternative version of this legend there were three coloured stones, red, white and green, each of which possessed different magical properties. The red stone would assist its owner to find favour with the person he or she most desired, the white stone if placed in the mouth would make its possessor beautiful, and the green stone would ensure safety to its owner.

Possibly because it flowers at about the time when the Swallows arrive and finally wilts at around the time of their departure, the Greater Celandine *(Chelidonium majus)* was a plant popularly believed to be connected in some mysterious way with the Swallow. In many places it was known as the Swallow herb and was widely believed to be capable of curing eye infections.

So strong was the belief in the curative powers of the Swallow that it frequently figured as one of the ingredients in various medical prescriptions. An old English recipe advised those suffering from any eye infection to prepare an ointment consisting of the ashes of Swallow mixed with honey, whilst to eat a Swallow's heart was not only a certain cure for the ague but also greatly improved the memory. In her *Stillroom Book* published in 1692 Mistress Jane Hussey recommended that her readers should 'take forty or fifty Swallows when they are ready to fly, bruise them to pieces in a mortar, feathers and all together, you should put them alive in the mortar. Add to them an ounce of castorum in powder, put all these in a still with white wine vinegar.' Such a concoction

23

she guaranteed was highly efficacious for dealing with 'passions of the heart, for the falling sickness, for sudden sound fits, for the dead palsie, apoplexies, lethargies and any other distemper of the head'. A Chinese recipe dating from the fourth century AD advised 'To use dragon's bone, first boil some aromatic herbs. Wash the bone twice in hot water, then reduce to powder and place in bags of thin stuff. Take two young Swallows and, after removing their entrails, stuff the bags into the Swallow and hang them over a spring. After one night take the bags out of the Swallows, remove the powder and mix it with a preparation for strengthening the kidneys.'

In contrast to all these rather vague theories one way in which the Swallow was of definite practical help to man was its use to convey the results of the chariot races held in Roman times. During the breeding season adult Swallows which were known to have young were captured and taken to the arena where the races were being held. Coloured threads which matched the winners' colours were tied to their legs and the birds immediately released. Anxious to return to their young, they would return straightaway to their nest, where men would be waiting to see by the colours on the birds' legs who were the winners.

Throughout the five continents in which it occurs the Swallow is universally highly regarded. Its grace, beauty and confiding nature together with its useful attribute of consuming large quantities of insect pests all combine to make the Swallow a particularly special bird whose annual arrival is anticipated with as much pleasure as the coming of spring.

FURTHER READING

Adams, L. E. G. 'Nest Records of the Swallow', *Bird Study*, volume 4, number 1 (1957).

Armstrong, E. A. *The Folklore of Birds*. Collins, London, 1957.

Bannerman, D. A. *The Birds of the British Isles*, volume 3. Oliver and Boyd, Edinburgh, 1954.

Bent, A. C. *Life Histories of North American Flycatchers, Larks, Swallows and their Families*. Smithsonian Institute, Washington, 1942.

Hare, C. E. *Bird Lore*. Country Life, London, 1952.

Mead, C. J. 'The Winter Quarters of British Swallows', *Bird Study*, volume 17, number 4 (1970).

Moller, Anders P. 'Breeding Habitat Selection in the Swallow', *Bird Study*, volume 30, number 2 (1983).

Moreau, R. E. *The Palearctic-African Bird Migration Systems*. Academic Press, London, 1972.

Purchon, R. E., et al. 'The Nesting Activities of the Swallow', *Proceedings of the Zoological Society of London*, volume 118 (1948).

Tate, P. *Swallows*. Witherby, London, 1981.

Turner, Angela. 'How Many Flies Make a Swallow?', *Birds*, volume 10, number 6 (1985).

Welty, J. C. *The Life of Birds*. Saunders, Philadelphia, 1962.

Witherby, H. F., et al. *The Handbook of British Birds*, volume 2. Witherby, London, 1938.

Zink, G. 'The Migration of European Swallows to Africa', *Ostrich*, supplement number 8 (1969).

ACKNOWLEDGEMENTS

Photographs are acknowledged as follows: P. Ginn, 16; Eric and David Hosking, 1, 4, 9, 10, 12, 13, 14, cover; Frank Lane Picture Agency Ltd, 3 (photograph by L. Lee Rue), 6 (photograph by Ronald Thompson), 7 (photograph by Roger Wilmshurst); Kenneth Newman, 17; Alan Parker, 5, 8, 11.